D1456830

MYSTERY PUZZLES

MYSTERY
PUZZLES

Devised by
Chris M. Dickson

With a foreword by
Victor Serebriakoff
Hon. President of International MENSA

BARNES
&NOBLE
B O O K S
NEW YORK

INTRODUCTION

By Victor Serebriakoff,
Hon. President of International MENSA

Here is a book of enigmas. Mind-stretching, thought-provoking, mystifying situations to get yourself hopelessly lost in. We are following a deliberate policy here. It's a calculated scheme to leave you, the victim reader, dazed, helpless and stunned. Chris Dickson's attitude is this: You asked for it, ya gonna get it. He is out to see you get it in full measure and running over.

No doubt your life runs along smooth tracks on well-oiled wheels so that you long for a challenge, a distraction to stir and excite your mind. If this is not so, then take my advice – just put this book down, attractive though it may seem, and go quietly away.

Challenge: Go into any library and count the number of titles under various categories. You will almost certainly find that the number of mystery novels outnumbers any other category. How can that be? Why do readers want to be confused, mystified and dragged into the affairs of a group of fictional characters who are being subjected to an incremental series of misfortunes?

You are led along one false track after another. You form a firm hypothesis which hardens into a theory as to who the mysterious serial killer is. Only, the villain turns out to be the next victim! So who the heck can it be now?

So let me try to see the point of view of you, the unfortunate reader, who has been lured by the spiced bait and has been hooked. You spend your hard-earned money to get this work of torture in your hands. Masochistically you begin to read, to get to know these strange characters. Your curious mind is attracted: you begin to identify with one character and detest another. But you are cautious, because you have been caught out before. You have found yourself liking the villain and hating the hero. You suspend your judgement and await disclosures. Eventually you get it right. You see the point, tear off the mask of mystery and stare triumphantly into what your sharp brain has revealed to you.

That is the moment when the "mountain moves" for you and a glow of quiet, restrained satisfaction flows into your mind. But who can you tell about it? To whom can you boast? No-one. Where can your impulsive shout of "Eureka!" be heard? Nowhere. The joy is private and yours alone to cuddle serenely to your happy heart.

But what if you look confidently to the answer page and find you have got it all wrong? The humiliation you have risked is upon you, and your midnight reveries are shattered. You become the clumsy, bumbling, over-confident police inspector of a hundred novels you have read where a dear old lady solves the crime that he cannot.

So, dear patient reader, take on these intractable problems that have been set for you. I, Victor Serebriakoff, an incurable puzzle setter, wish you good luck and the adequate degree of success that is more pleasing than victories that come too easily. Go to it then.

A player takes three shots at this target. His second shot is closer to the bull's eye than his first, and his third shot is closer to the bull's eye than his second.

He needs over 80 points to win a prize. After a significant amount of negotiation, the stall keeper agrees that his total score for three shots is 85.

What was the dispute about, and what did he score with each shot?

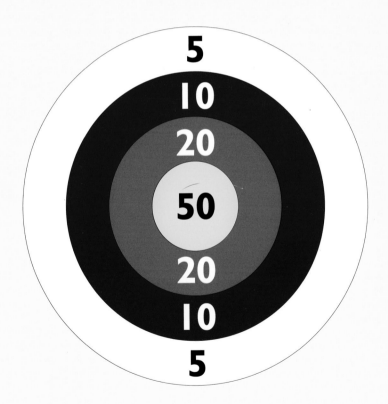

I own a team of two drivers in the dangerous and competitive world of International Tractor Racing.

I have agreed this bonus payment schedule with my two drivers:

1st place = $40,000
2nd place = $30,000
3rd place = $20,000
4th place = $10,000

One of the drivers recently came third in a race. What reasonable argument did he use to convince me that he should be paid $30,000 for his efforts?

Winston Churchill was Prime Minister of Great Britain during part of the 1940s and 1950s.

He once appeared suddenly in a cloakroom when there were several ladies "adjusting their dress". Despite a slight amount of commotion for a while, there were no press reports of this incident, and it did not cause any damage to his political career.

Given the morals and attitudes of the day, this could be seen as quite surprising. However, the whole incident can be explained away because...

What?

The only person in the house at the time of the theft, apart from the victim, wealthy heiress Miss Pandora, was Cunning Reg.

As I cross-examined him, his alibi seemed watertight; he was able to produce convincing papers to certify he was a qualified electrician, and it's true that an electrician was correcting a fault in the wiring in the house at that time.

I was having a hard time trying to pin the crime on him, and my assistant brought some mugs of hot tea in during a break in the enquiry.

I joked to Reg that he ought not to steal my special mug, and sipped the brew down. Suddenly I worked out why Reg couldn't possibly have been an electrician, and started to look for further holes in his story.

What was the piece of evidence that incriminated him?

How did a snake cause a perfectly seaworthy boat to sink in a matter of moments?

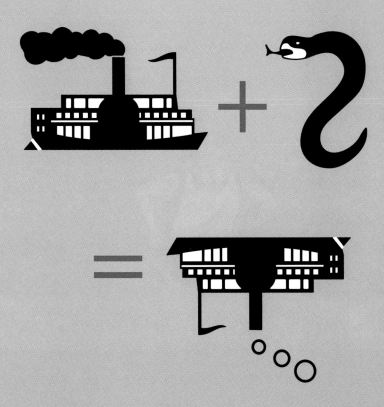

I own a running track with two concentric lanes for the two runners. It's a full three seconds quicker (per lap) to run round the inside lane than the outside lane.

Alan and Andy agree to settle their differences about which one of the two is the quicker runner by having a two-lap race, but they can't settle their differences about which one of them should enjoy the advantage of the inside lane.

We don't have any timing equipment to measure how long each one takes in each lane, so can you suggest a solution that will produce a fair two-lap race to decide which one is quicker?

Last year I went to Hawaii for my holidays. As I had not been there before, I asked three friends – namely Wilhelmina Neumann, Luke Manilow and Pauline Emmanuel – who had been there before for travel advice.

All three of them recommended a particular local man who, they said, was an extremely reliable and efficient taxi driver who knew the island well. He would be able to take me to my hotel for a small fee and thus get my holiday off to a good start.

However, when I arrived in the airport on Hawaii it took me a long time to find the driver with whom I had made arrangements beforehand by telephone. It turns out that he had been waiting there when I landed, but I couldn't make out the sign he had made which had my name on it.

What factor had made my experiences different from that of my friends?

A wealthy Japanese music promoter had heard that a very famous American rock star was flying into his country shortly. He wanted to meet the star desperately. However, he also wanted to have his picture taken when the rock star arrived at the airport, so that he would appear in the publicity photographs in the next day's newspapers.

Unfortunately, the vantage point used by the press meant that the photographers would take their photos when the rock star came through the customs area. He asked the officials if he would be allowed into the Customs area for the purposes of the photo, but they said that would break strict international laws.

How did the music promoter get around the problem?

The headline below, and several others like it, were seen in a number of different newspapers in the UK.

Although there was mourning for some while, there was no police investigation, murder enquiry or coroner's reports. Furthermore, nothing more was heard of this story after this day.

What were the circumstances of this death?

CROWDS IN TEARS AS ONE MAN SHOT DEAD IN TRAGEDY

When a friend of mine was moving into his new flat, he had two pictures to put on the wall.

His father measured the whole wall, which turned out to be 6 yards long. So they put the hooks in at 2 and 4 yards along the wall to distribute the pictures evenly.

But somehow, when I look at the pictures they didn't seem to be spaced quite right.

What had gone wrong?

On a yacht, it is quite common to haul up a man to the top of mast – to fix a problem with the rigging, for example. A rope is tied around a volunteer while several other people haul them up to the top (as illustrated).

However, because the rope was so heavy, in the past it was quite possible for the rope on the left (X) to outweigh the rope (Y) and volunteer (V). When his happens, the heavier left side pulls the lighter right side upwards, and the poor volunteer is propelled towards the pulley at great speed. This often caused severe injuries.

What *extremely simple* safety measure was introduced so that such injuries did not occur in future?

With thanks to Mark Hawkins

X

Y

V

X>Y+V

I was given a pet turtle that was born on the 29th of February in the year 1992, and I expect it to live at least 150 years. I shall surely not live that long, but my great-grandchildren who will eventually look after it might.

If its first birthday was on the 29th of February in the year 1996, when will its thirtieth birthday be?

It was my birthday, and I had a big cake in the shape of a cube, each side a foot long. Including me and Cunning Reg, there were 23 people in the house.

They all wanted a piece of the cake, exactly the same size and all exactly the same shape as the original cake. I had difficulty working out how to cut the cake with my knife into 23 identical pieces.

Then Reg lived up to his name, and went and got something that made cutting the cake a lot easier.

What did he bring?

Cunning Reg was walking through the peaceful, law-abiding town of Menagerie, inhabited by identical-looking Verities, who always tell the truth, and Perfids, who always lie.

He was suddenly met by an inhabitant who said "I am a Logical Mugger. If the next statement you make is true, I shall take your watch; if the next statement you make is false, I shall take your wallet."

Cunning Reg was then able to tell whether the inhabitant was a Verity or a Perfid, but can you?

OR

Cunning Reg and Confused Alan each bought a $3 double whisky from the bar.

Reg said to Alan, "I bet you $1 you can't drink your double whisky in one go."

Alan said to Reg, trying to trick Reg out of a cheap drink, "I bet you $2 that I can't drink your double whisky in one go."

Reg replied "I bet you $3 that I take that bet!" By this point, Alan was thoroughly confused.

Should he take Reg's latest bet?

Berry and Benny have reached the final of a pool competition, which consists of playing up to five games of pool. Whoever wins three games wins the prize of $300.

Berry wins the first game, Benny wins the second and Berry wins the third. At this point, the fire alarm goes off and the match cannot continue.

How should the prize money be split between Berry and Benny?

Papadopulis Dodson, awful versifier extraordinaire and founder of the *Penultimate Poem Plant* (motto: "Doggerel on Demand"), was found poisoned in his chair.

The only other people in the house at the time were Cunning Reg, Confused Alan, Miss Pandora, Benny and Berry. Clearly the poison had quickly robbed him of his strength because he didn't try to alert anyone before his demise, though he did leave a curious note by his side, illustrated below.

"Not one of his best limericks; it hardly even rhymes," said Cunning Reg. "Perhaps the poison affected his linguistic talents." However, it did contain a clue to the poisoner's identity.

Can you tell whodunnit?

There was a young girl from Rugby
Who, by ten, had a Uni degree.
She soon made her mark
On science, but hark,
This tale is just pure fantasye!

Cunning Reg took a coin from his pocket and showed it, head-side up, to Confused Alan.

He said, "I bet that if I turn this perfectly ordinary coin over, there'll still be a head facing up." Alan, naturally enough, said "If that's a perfectly normal coin with one head side and one tail side, I bet that there'll be a tail on the other side."

Reg replied "It is a perfectly ordinary coin – look, I'll prove it." He proved it was an ordinary coin; then, as he said he would, he turned the coin over to reveal a head side face up.

How did he prove it was an ordinary coin and make the bet work?

Being so impressed with the previous trick, Alan has appointed Reg to design the coins to be used in the country of Pandistan.

Reg has had the "bright" idea of making the coins have an even number of sides. "After all," says Reg, "every other nation's coins are either circular or have an odd number of sides, so these coins will be very distinctive!"

What's the good reason why coins generally have an odd number of sides?

Cunning Reg presented a cocktail that he had made to Confused Alan. It was made up of clear liquid, but had an ice cube floating half-way between the surface of the drink and the bottom of the glass.

"Is it drinkable?" asked Alan. Reg replied, "Of course it is, although I have had to prepare that drink in a special sort of way."

How had Reg prepared this "Levitating Ice Cube" cocktail?

Berry and Benny are about to perform a delicate chemical experiment, but need to protect their hands to avoid touching the chemicals.

Berry has brought along four very simple rubber gloves, but Benny points out that they're all designed to be worn on the left hand.

What can Berry do so that they can both work together on the experiment without using any additional equipment?

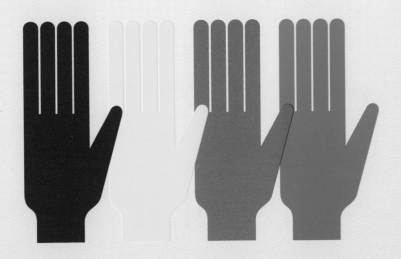

Cunning Reg and his friend, Confused Alan, went to the fair.

First, they went to a booth where Alan collected the autograph who claimed that no man was stronger than him. After that, they went to a booth where they saw a man who similarly claimed to be the weakest man in the world; Alan collected his autograph as well.

Finally, they went to a booth where they saw a man who claimed to be the second strongest man in the world and Alan got his third autograph of the day. "I was expecting that man would be called Norman," said Alan to Reg.

Why?

Cunning Reg fills a bucket with as much water as he possibly can, and uses a set of special equipment to let him take it outside, down the garden path, across the road, over the bridge, round the park and all the way to the statue without spilling even the tiniest bit of it. However, clouds fill the sky, and eventually it starts to rain.

Why does the bucket not overflow as soon as the first raindrop lands inside it?

One day, a man is sitting at home. After thinking for some time, he decides to shoot himself in the knee with a gun he has managed to obtain.

He has no intention of killing himself. In fact, he has worked out that this is the best thing to do to help improve his situation.

Why did he do such a dangerous thing?

A new ship had just been constructed, and everything had pretty much gone to plan.

However, near the end of production, someone spotted that the letters on the small sign displaying the ship's name had been put on back to front.

As a result, tens of millions of US dollars had to be spent correcting the error.

How could such a small mistake cost so much money?

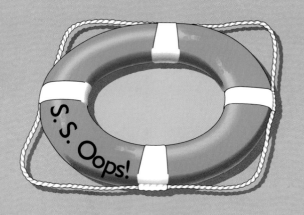

Prince Rasulu of Nigeria visited Bogota, Colombia, in 1994. He was given the decorous diplomatic treatment appropriate for a visiting VIP, including the attention of the Minister for Foreign Affairs for two days. In return, he gave several press conferences and was interviewed by a number of newspapers.

However, once he had left the country, the officials realized that they had made a mistake.

What had they forgotten?

Police are often able to track burglars who don't cover their tracks properly. For example, it is possible to follow any trails that are left behind. A standard technique, when there is fresh snow outside the burgled property, is to follow the trail of footprints left behind by the thieves as they make their getaway.

However, police answered a call from a burgled store one snowy day and found no footprints or other tracks in the snow at all, although it was established that no snow had fallen since the burglary.

Whom did the police hold responsible for the crime?

Police are on the trail of a notorious drug smuggler most infamous for his ability to slip from one town to the next, even slipping from one country to another without being noticed.

The distinctive features about this smuggler are that he brags to the local police who have failed to catch him every time he leaves a country, and that he spends a week in each town before moving on. The towns he has most recently visited, in order, are Helsinki, Melbourne, Rome, Tokyo, Mexico City and Munich.

Where can he be expected to appear next?

Evil Reg was personally responsible for the death of Mr. Victor Timothy. Reg did not perform the killing in person and in fact had not seen Timothy for three years before. Nevertheless, he managed to send the murder weapon safely through the post to him along with a greeting card.

Timothy died by using the weapon in the manner it was intended to be used. The card ended up touching the murder weapon, but the greeting card never reached its intended destination.

How did Reg kill Timothy?

Confused Alan is responsible for dredging a canal to remove all the rusting fridges, bicycles, cars and wheelbarrows that have been dumped in it and got tangled up at the canal's muddy bottom.

He pledges that he will remove all the rubbish, but Cunning Reg tells him of an item that he must take very great care not to remove from the canal.

What is it?

A firm advertises its product for sale in a magazine, and hundreds of people send money to the firm to buy the product.

However, the firm decides that it can't sell the product, and so it sends all the applicants their money back in the form of company banker's drafts.

However, many of the drafts are not cashed, and so the firm made a profit while not actually selling anything.

Why?

Two men storm into a store and start taking all the stock off the shelves by scooping it into large black bags.

However, the staff do not look too worried and the owners of the store (who were not insured) were not greatly financially affected by the raid, apart from a little lost custom, a small time for restocking and the inconvenience.

Why did the two men not get what they bargained for?

A man walks to a bus stop and asks a lady there for directions. The woman has never seen this man before. There is nothing offensive in the man's actions, and he appears to be pleasant and smartly dressed.

The woman suddenly turns to the other people at the bus stop and asks them to help her perform a citizen's arrest on him. For a little while, the other people in the queue are reluctant to get involved. However, once the lady explains her motive the others act quickly to restrain the man before he runs away.

Why did the woman want the man stopped?

A robber drives up to a remote post office in the town of Cariato, Italy. He parks his car and rushes into his target building and demands large amounts of money from the post office teller.

With the money safely in his possession, his plan to make a swift getaway backfires due to some unexpected intervention and he is easily caught.

What mistake had he made?

We stay in Italy for our next story, this time from the town of Cosenza.

A man is organizing a "stag night" party for the groom the night before a wedding, and hires a dancer to make a dramatic entrance at the party. However, the lady in question is conspicuous by her absence and is later found to have died in the process of making her surprise entrance.

How did she die?

A pair of brothers are involved in a murder, and it is known that one of them actually perpetrated the crime. In the country where this murder took place, the death penalty is still used for convicted murderers only.

How did the brothers collude to escape the death penalty, receiving lesser periods in jail for a more minor offence instead?

A C.B. operator was constructing a radio mast in his back yard. During the course of the day, he had carried some tools and sections of lightweight girders to the top of the mast.

Rather than carry them down individually, the man put all his equipment into a wooden barrel that was attached to a pulley system, where the pulley was at the top of the mast and the other end of the rope was securely tied off on the ground.

Once the man had released the rope on the ground, the radio fan sustained these three major injuries at approximate five second intervals: major cuts to the hands, broken ribs, and a large blow to the head by a blunt object.

Can you work out the sequence of events that followed?

Things had not been going too well for Mr and Mrs Gerrard over the past few months. They had lost their long-term family pet, Mrs Gerrard had lost her part-time job and they had money problems too.

Often, their budget was very tight. Mr Gerrard had sold his car and walks to work each day. Mrs Gerrard drove the remaining car to get the shopping. She went nearly every day to try to get the best bargains. However, sometimes Mrs Gerrard would run out of petrol and not have enough money to buy some more. In these cases, Mr Gerrard would have to ask one of the locals to tow her home, which was naturally an embarrassing situation to be in.

Suddenly, one day Mr Gerrard was extremely glad that the car ran out of petrol.

Can you think in what unusual, but not extremely rare, circumstances someone would be pleased about running out of petrol?

Cunning Reg took another tissue and blew hard.

"That sounds like a nasty cold you've got there," said Confused Alan.

"Yes," said Reg, "I've just been on a photography trip to the Arctic. It's a beautiful unspoiled landscape to film. We spent three weeks filming the ridges and ice packs around one area bordering on the Arctic Circle.

"However, the second week there wasn't too good – I got frostbite, I lost some of the nails from my toes, and I contracted this darn cold into the bargain. I'm getting over the worst of it now, though. Thanks for your concern."

A fine story, except that...?

The mayor of a Norwegian town was due to make an official visit to the English town with which his town was "twinned". One of the town hall officials made the necessary arrangements with the facilities managers at a nearby conference venue.

The big day came and the Norwegian mayor arrived right on time, to be greeted by the civic dignitaries from England.

However, the music played over the speaker system didn't sound right at all. Instead of drums and trumpets, there was organ music, the sound of an excited crowd, and cries of "Roll up, roll up!"

Can you see how the mix-up occurred?

A man crashed through the window of a skyscraper and fell a from a great height to his death.

The police had established these facts: the man had not lost his footing, and was in good health. A group of visitors were with the man at the time when the man ran through the pane of glass.

After talking to some colleagues of the dead man, they soon discovered that this was a terrible accident, rather than suicide.

What were the circumstances?

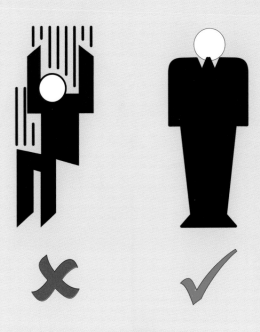

Cunning Reg is sitting quietly alone at a table with a book in front of him. He is running his finger across the book, and enjoying its contents.

However, Cunning Reg cannot read Braille, or any similar tactile language. Furthermore, there are no lights in the room.

How is he reading the book?

As you probably know, the Bible is full of stories about plagues, war and destruction.

According to the Bible, who is the only person who has killed a quarter of the world's population?

A man had been earning some extra money by cleaning the windows of office blocks in the city for over three years.

One day, he was cleaning a particular office block. Although he was cleaning all the windows diligently and in the proper manner, from that day onwards his weekly income dropped substantially.

What caused this drop in living standards?

Confused Alan has just gone to a bakery to buy 240 bread rolls for the restaurant that he works for.

After giving his order to the bakery, he comes back with twenty bread rolls too many.

What mistake did he make?

In Texas, a hall contains several dozen senior citizens playing bingo. However, that day there is a particular run of false "Full House" calls.

The players get increasingly irritated with the caller and threaten to attack him. In the end, the police have to be called for the caller's own protection.

What was the problem with the day's play?

A luxurious ocean liner strikes an iceberg, has its hull torn open beneath the waterline and sinks. However, when the iceberg strikes, the wireless radio operator on board starts tapping out a three-letter signal repeatedly in Morse code.

Half-way through the night, the signal changes to a different three letters. Why?

In a court case, it was alleged that the defendant had seriously assaulted a woman while she was in her own home, and then left the house before setting it on fire. As it happened, the alarm was raised in time and the woman escaped to live another day.

The defendant's wife and family were in the courtroom to provide their support and act as character witnesses.

It did not take the jury too long to make up their minds from the evidence presented to them. The man was found guilty of attempted murder and subsequently sentenced to eight years in prison.

However, the woman who was assaulted began to cry and wail, even though the guilty man would be out of circulation for some years.

Why was she so upset?

Benny was looking after his aged sleeping Auntie Betty when Berry burst through the door, excitedly showing off his new invention. "It's a set of weighing scales to measure a person's weight to the nearest tenth of a gram!", said Berry.

Benny said he was impressed and stood on it. However, the weight it displayed kept flickering up and down by twenty or thirty grams, even when Benny stood as still as he could.

They then tried to weigh Auntie Betty; Benny decided to move the chair she was sitting on onto the scales, and then weigh the chair separately later once Betty had moved.

However, once they had lifted Betty and the chair on top of the scales, the reading was constant and remained so for more than thirty seconds as she remained completely motionless. Why?

Indianapolis is a city in the United States of America that is part of the Eastern Time Zone, although it's in a region of the US referred to as the Mid-West. New York is another city in the same time zone.

Every week at 5pm on Thursday, Berry in New York rings a certain public telephone box in Indianapolis where it's answered by his cousin Bessie who doesn't have a telephone in her own home.

However, once a year Berry rings the telephone box, but Bessie never answers it. Why?

"Hello... anyone there...?"

See if you can complete this unusual story:

A woman tried to rob a Florida hotel with a rather unusual weapon. She entered the front foyer of the hotel brandishing a real chainsaw.

As you might expect, a commotion started, and the staff began to put together the money that was held at reception.

In fact, everything was going to her plan until an eagle-eyed hotel resident spotted that...?

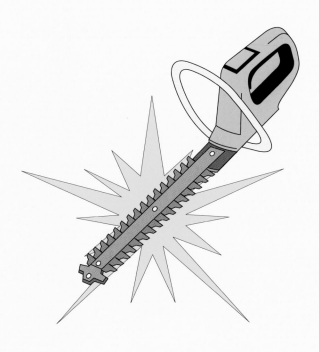

John Wycliffe was a 14th Century theologian from Oxford who played an important part in history before the Reformation. He wrote a series of articles which attacked the Church and its claim to authority.

These claims were seen as heretical, and he was later burned at the stake on the orders of the Council of Constance.

However, he felt no pain when this happened. Before his death, he was in good health and he did not have any disease (such as leprosy) which would numb the pain.

Why didn't Wycliffe suffer at the stake?

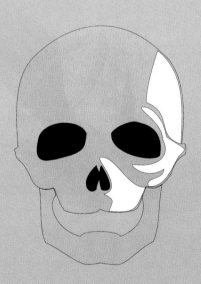

An American couple were living in Singapore for a year, along with their children and pet dog.

The couple, who were not yet fluent in the local lingo, were keen to try the local delicacies, but motioned to the waiter a request for the dog and children to have something simpler to eat. The waiter duly brought out some beefburgers, and led the dog into the kitchen.

By the end of the meal, the couple were feeling extremely upset and unwell, all because of a very sad misunderstanding. There was nothing wrong with the food they had eaten because it had been prepared to the best hygienic standards.

What was the misunderstanding, and what was making the couple feel so unwell?

In the dead of night, a man threw a brick through a shop window and stole some valuable jewels.

An hour later, the police arrived to survey the scene. They tested the brick, the broken glass and the rest of the shop display but no imprints of the thief's fingers could be found anywhere.

However, they were still able to identify and convict the guilty man, by only using fingerprint evidence in court.

How come?

The diaries of Samuel Pepys contained accounts of the Great Fire of London, as well other events in London in the 17th Century.

These important diaries were easily discovered days after Pepys's death. However, it was at least 150 years before any historical benefit was obtained from these documents.

Why?

A man had the contents of his car stolen: his wallet, house keys, pager, stereo radio and some personal effects.

However, with some ingenuity, he managed to concoct a plan. Without a struggle he trapped the culprit, who was prosecuted successfully for handling stolen goods.

How was the trap set?

A particularly interesting competition, which has been run in a number of different national newspapers, has the following rules:

(1) Entrants must pick a number between 1 and 100 inclusive (no fractions).

(2) The winner is the person who picks the number that is two-thirds of the average number chosen by all the entries.

What number would you choose?

01	02	03	04	05	06	07	08	09	10
11	12	13	14	15	16	17	18	19	20
21	22	23	24	25	26	27	28	29	30
31	32	33	34	35	36	37	38	39	40
41	42	43	44	45	46	47	48	49	50
51	52	53	54	55	56	57	58	59	60
61	62	63	64	65	66	67	68	69	70
71	72	73	74	75	76	77	78	79	80
81	82	83	84	85	86	87	88	89	90
91	92	93	94	95	96	97	98	99	100

You would have thought, in these days of opportunity for all, that prejudice against left-handed people was a thing of the past.

However, there was one man who wanted to do something, but he was not allowed to do it for safety reasons. The explanation given was he was left-handed, and everyone else doing this activity locally was right-handed.

In the end, he gathered together seven other left-handed people in the same situation, so that finally he was able to perform this activity.

What activity did the man have a longing to do?

The burglar would always target the same kind of properties: flats on the ground floor. Each time, he would listen to see if anyone was in, and then break in through the window in order to steal electrical equipment. It was clear that the culprit had worn gloves to conceal fingerprints, and there were no clues inside the flat that were of any use.

The spate of robberies continued until an astute officer managed to make a connection between the crimes that the burglar hadn't accounted for.

What caused the criminal's downfall?

A man, a car mechanic by trade, was perfectly happy with the way his "Mini" car looked.

However, one day he decided to lower the suspension by two inches. He also changed the wheels to a smaller diameter, saving another two inches in height.

Finally, with the help of a friend who was a panel-beater, they resculpted the top of the car so that the roof was now six inches lower than it used to be.

Although this made the car more uncomfortable for the driver, over the course of the next few weeks all the effort was already saving him a lot of money.

Why did the man go to all the trouble to minimalize his car?

Wesley was camping alone in the woods one day, when a fly got stuck in his ear. He unwisely put his finger in his ear to try to dislodge it, but succeeded only in driving the insect further in.

Due to the discomfort caused by the insect wriggling around in his ear, he looked around urgently for anything that might help him.

Which of the objects illustrated did he use to solve the problem?

One day, Susan went riding at her local stables. Her usual horse was not available because someone else was using it at the time, so she rode another horse instead.

Everything was fine, until something startled the animal. Not being used to handling this particular beast, nothing Susan could do helped to calm the horse, which began to career dangerously towards a large fence.

Thinking quickly, what action did Susan take which she knew would bring the horse to a complete stop without fail?

A man was skiing down a mountain in California on a thick, foam pad that he had obtained.

Sadly, the man died after he crashed into a post used to support part of the ski lift. Upon hearing the story, however, the locals were not very sympathetic with the late man's demise.

Why?

A man buys a new car to go alongside his current one. However, he is unlucky and doesn't get one of the car registration numbers he was looking for.

The registration he is looking for isn't personalized, and doesn't have any special interpretation or connotation, and there are millions of them available. So, he makes the necessary payments and arrangements with the authorities to change the registration to something else.

Can you think in what practical, everyday circumstances this might happen?

Police had been following a particular suspect for several days. The man in question had been seen several times loitering around vending areas, and the policemen were convinced that he was responsible for a number of vending machine thefts in the area.

The police arrested the man on suspicion of theft. They were about to release him on bail pending further investigation, when the thief made a rather foolish error. He didn't admit to the thefts, but the police now had enough circumstantial evidence to formally charge him.

What was the mistake?

A school ran an trekking expedition to Africa, but it was not long before they got totally lost. Their leader was using a standard compass to find their way. It was later found that the compass was working normally, and that any other compass would have given the same readings.

However, when the rescue services had located the group, it appeared that they had trekked in almost entirely the wrong direction. The group leader was sure he was using the correct part of the compass needle (i.e. Red points to North).

They were not near any electromagnets or other artificial interference, so how else could the trek have gone wrong?

Trading standards officials were caught out when they tried to take legal action against a company producing liquid fabric softener. The trading officials claimed that the company was making a new claim on its packaging that implied that the consumer was getting a better deal, when in fact the price, quantity and quality of the product had remained completely unchanged.

However, the court action failed when it was adjudged that the manufacturers had in fact made a perfectly true statement. Furthermore, the softener company had acted correctly both legally and morally.

Can you think what the claim might have been?

Mrs Benn is the landlady of a block of apartments. One of the residents, Mr Edgar, asks her to wake him at 6am and retires early. He bolts and secures the mortice lock on his door and goes to sleep.

However, when he can't be roused the next morning, Mrs Benn in alarm seeks the help of a nearby friend, Mr Dax. Mr Dax charges the door open, breaking the lock and bolt. They find that the key is still in the lock and Mr Edgar is lying in bed, dead by strangulation.

There was no-one else hiding in the room, no chimney, or other doors and all the windows were locked from the inside.

Could it have been murder?

A team of artists are constructing a new mural made up of 200 segments. Each segment of the wall is 1 yard long and made from a large slab of painted concrete.

As the segments are so heavy, and must be joined together sequentially, the artists have laid out the segments in the correct order beforehand, in a line along the required route.

Starting at the first segment, the artists begin to join one segment to the next in line, forming a continuous picture. The plan starts well, but they soon wish they had done things a differently.

There were no technical difficulties with their tools, and the ground is good and firm. What was it about their organization of the process that caused them problems?

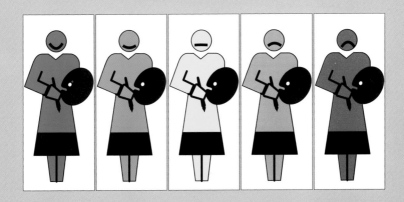

A man chooses to sleep in a tent, by himself, for a few hours. He chooses this form of accommodation, even though he has a nice comfy bed available. It is raining heavily outside. The tent does not offer much in the way of warmth or protection from any bad weather.

Furthermore, the man continues to keep going into the tent several times a month. Some of his friends are unsure whether this is good for his health.

What are the circumstances that would explain this?

Each year the small town of Jamestown elects a May Queen at their annual fair.

"And what other members are there in your family?" asked the compere of the fair. "I have two sisters and three brothers," said the May Queen.

The May Queen's elder sister was taking part in a bowling competition on the other side of town. By coincidence, she was asked the same question, to which she replied "I have one sister and four brothers."

But surely that's impossible, isn't it?

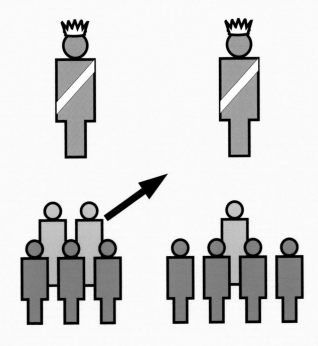

A woman sets off on her horse for a half-hour ride through the countryside.

She takes her time to ensure she chooses the correct route, and that the horse does not hurt itself or fall.

When she arrives at her destination, she is only a few seconds later than she had intended. However, this makes her extremely angry.

She is not a betting woman, so what else might explain this sequence of events?

The Chief of Police was bemused when doing an analysis of the crime statistics along the string of beaches they patrol. It seemed that one particular beach had a very poor score in terms of the proportion of crimes that were solved.

She made some further analysis of the area, but could not see any obvious reasons why that particular beach was so difficult to solve crimes in. The problem was not due to an underperforming officer either, since all policeman took turns to patrol the beaches.

She then visited the beach and immediately saw what the reason was.

Can you guess?

I am in the 23rd floor of a skyscraper. I walk 100 yards down a corridor, and I am surprised to find that, according to the sign on the wall, I am now on the 29th floor. I double-check by asking a passer-by, who confirms that I am now on floor 29 but have come from floor 23.

This is mysterious, as I have not used any stairs or lifts during that short walk. Nor have I walked up or down any ramp or sloped surface of any kind.

Is this possible? If so, how?

Inspector Murphy arrived at the station just in time to catch some criminals. After taking their names and addresses, and logging them in his notebook, he returned to his usual patrol.

Later in the day, Murphy walked by a vagrants selling illegal goods. He called his superiors to let them know what was happening, but he didn't do anything about the situation himself.

Despite this, Murphy's boss was very happy at the way he handled the problem. Why?

A man stopped his car in order to buy a newspaper in the shop across the road. However, as there was no other spaces available, he parked in a no-parking zone.

After purchasing his paper, he returned to find that a parking penalty notice had been affixed to his car. After reading the notice, he laughed out loud.

Even though the ticket was filled out correctly, and he had to pay the fine, why did the man so amused by the situation?

The legs of my chair are broken. Of the remaining stumps, one leg is two inches shorter than the other three.

Luckily, I have some cuboidal wooden blocks of various lengths, and I want to use them to rebuild the legs so that they are all the same length. There are eight blocks in all, of length 3, 4, 5, 6, 7, 8, 9 and 10 inches.

After a lot of trial and error, I finally find a combination of blocks which leaves all the legs of my chair level.

How do I do it?

Cunning Reg's father owns a clock shop and specializes in clocks which chime out the passing of time.

Many of his clocks chime 24 times every day. However, others chime 156 times and a few chime 180 times. In fact, one of his clocks chimes 228 times every day!

Yet Reg's father is very happy with all the clocks in his shop and knows they are all working properly, despite different clocks chiming different number of times.

Why?

"I saw the criminal you're looking for from behind; he was carrying eight balloons. Each one had a letter on. I can't remember what the letters were, but they spelt a word which I guess is where he got them from.

"The balloon that was closest to me burst, but the others still spelt a word, suggesting what he would be doing later that night with his drinking associates. A second balloon burst, the wind blew them about, and they formed a word indicating what sort of language he would use.

"Another balloon burst, the balloons bobbed about and revealed the first thing he had done this morning. Then, after the next burst, it spelt a word that suggested what he had stolen from the field. When the fifth balloon popped, the remaining three juggled to suggest where he would be headed. One of those burst, leaving a clue to his job that would help him where he was headed. Then a seventh one burst, leaving only the first."

What do we know about the man in question?

Police had been called to the scene of the crime – a bank on the outskirts of town.

A lady employee of the bank explained that a man had come up to her window. He had tried to make it look like he was really withdrawing some cash, so as not to arouse suspicion from anyone else in the bank. The piece of paper he handed to her had scrawled on it: "THIS IS A HOLD UP. GIVE ME LOTS OF MONEY IN A BAG AND YOU WON'T GET HURT."

The police looked at the robber's note and laughed. Without the need for fingerprint tests, looking at the security videos, handwriting analysis or any other scene-of-crime detective work, the culprit was caught within the hour.

What was the crook's stupid mistake?

Berry and Benny, sickened by all the distressing things that have happened to them, have decided to play Russian roulette until one of them dies.

The deadly game will decide their fate. The rules are:

1. *A simple "Heads or Tails" coin toss using a fair coin decides who gets the gun first.*

2. *The player without the gun turns his back on the person with the gun.*

3. *The player with the gun spins the barrel until it stops somewhere at random. (The gun has six chambers, one of which contains the bullet.)*

4. *The player with the gun pulls the trigger while aiming directly at the back of the other player.*

5. *If the player being aimed at does not die, he gets the gun and steps 2 to 4 are repeated until someone dies.*

An independent adjudicator will observe to ensure that no-one breaks these rules. How could either player maximize his chances of survival?

A truck driver drives down a main road at 90 m.p.h. The speed limit is clearly advertised as 70 m.p.h., and soon the truck attracts the attention of the police.

A fleet of seven squad cars accompanies the truck down the main road in order to warn other motorists of the danger. The police urge the driver to stop the vehicle. Eventually, it comes to a stop and the driver emerges from the truck.

However, the man was released without further questioning and was not charged with any offence. Why?

Two ocean-going ships, each flying their national flag, spot each other from a distance, abandon their original journeys and sail towards each other as quickly as they can.

When they near each other, their officers then realize that they had both jumped to the same incorrect conclusion, laugh about it with one another and part amicably.

What countries were the two ships from, and what error had they made?

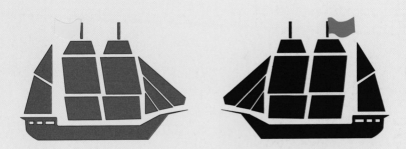

A bank offers a mortgage that seems to be too good to be true – whenever the country's central bank raises interest rates, the bank would **lower** the variable rate of their mortgage. Although the reverse was also true, this deal was offered at a time when interest rates were very low, and the outlook for the next 25 years was almost certainly that interest rates were going to go up.

The initial rate of the mortgage was fairly competitive, compared with those of other banks, and this bank obtained a lot of new customers from this deal.

Given that the bank is still trading today, how did they manage to offer this seemingly risk-free gamble?

At the same time every week, Fred would return home to have a shower after playing squash at his local sports complex.

After five weeks he had enough proof to conclude that his wife was probably having an affair with another man, even though nothing had been added, removed or left behind in the house, not even hair, fingerprints, etc.

How come?

At the International Convention of Philosophers and Logicians held in the oriental city Phu-Liu, I introduced myself to a new delegate.

He didn't reply but handed me a business card inscribed on one side like this:

> **My name is Bill Brewer.**
> **The statement on the other**
> **side of this card is TRUE.**

and inscribed on the other side like this:

> **My name is Bill Stewart.**
> **The statement on the other**
> **side of this card is FALSE.**

What can you say about his name?

Benny sells the only type of chocolate bar available in Menagerie in his shop. He has a large stock of bars and makes sure to keep at least 1000 in stock at all times.

Whenever someone buys bars from his shop, he makes a note of how many bars they bought, and at the end of the year, he makes a list of how many times each number of bars is bought.

His list one year shows that whilst lots of people bought 7 bars of chocolate or more (in fact, one customer bought 84!) and lots of customers bought 5 bars of chocolate or less, no customer ever seemed to buy bars six at a time.

What is the most likely explanation for this?

It was a stressful and traumatic day for the couple involved. With much sorrow, they divorced within a few hours of their getting married.

This is not the first time such an incident had happened. However, they are still married to one another even though they have not married anyone else since their only divorce.

How can this be possible?

A man is arrested for drunkenness and is taken into custody for the night by the police.

Once he had completely sobered up, he went to work the next morning. However, it was not long before he found himself back in the same police cell. The man did not protest, however, although he knew he had done nothing wrong this time.

What was going on?

A building is being sold by a property agent.

There are no windows in the building, and the size is just seventeen feet by seven feet. There are no running water or sewerage facilities, and there is only one electricity power point.

There are no plans to redevelop any part of this property or the surrounding area.

Despite all this, the property agent has no problem selling the building for an extremely high price. What's going on?

Cunning Reg was having some difficulties getting good service out of his local government authority. The street lights in his area were very rarely working, and the ones that were working were either very dim or flickering badly.

Despite a barrage of telephone calls, letters, faxes and emails aimed towards his council, nothing was done to repair the damage, regardless of whether Reg was curteous or forthright in his tone. Then Cunning Reg had an idea.

After a simple, pleasant phone call to the council, workmen were around to fix the lights within 24 hours.

What did Reg say that caused the desired result?

An eight-year-old boy is driving his parents' car down a public highway. Naturally, a number of the other drivers on the road become concerned and alert the police.

After instruction from the police escort, the boy brings the car to a stop. However, he is not charged, cautioned or even told off.

Why?

After finishing work at her office, a would-be starlet goes to a model agency for a tryout. Sadly, they say that she is not tall enough to become a model.

However, the next morning she goes back to the same agency for another tryout and this time she is accepted for exactly the same job as she was trying for the previous day. She is not wearing anything that would increase her height, such as different shoes or a wig. Also, she was measured in exactly the same way both times.

How did she manage to achieve her ambition?

In an American state, the local officials passed a law which, they thought, would make their children's education in mathematics much simpler.

In fact, this law was not only wrong, but it could have been potentially very dangerous.

What was the law?

A native Italian emigrates to England and looks for a place to live. He finds a lovely house in the countryside, with large fields, a stable and an outdoor swimming pool. The man is extremely keen to buy the property, and the deal is struck.

However, when it comes to exchanging the contracts, there appears to be a problem. The man has only a fraction of the money required to buy the house.

If the man knew that he would have to pay for the house in pounds sterling, not Italian lira, where else did the confusion arise?

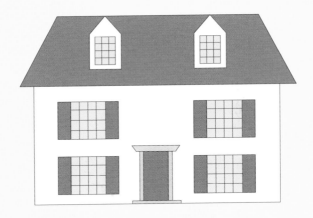

A number of cars, at least twenty, are speeding along public roads. They are breaking the speed limit for that area.

Despite the fact that there are quite a number of witnesses, no complaints were made to the police. Even if someone had complained, it is highly unlikely that the police would do anything. In fact, they probably already knew about it!

What was going on?

ANSWERS

Many of the stories in this book are pure flights of fantasy, but others are based on actual events. It is virtually impossible to attest to the truth of these stories, and as such definitive sources have not been quoted.

Where a story has been based, at least in part, by true events, the acronym BOATS (Based On A True Story) precedes the answer.

ANSWERS TO PUZZLES ENDING IN –1

1 The second and third bullets scored 20 and 50. The player's first bullet landed right on the border between 20 and 10. He argued to the stall keeper that taking the average (15) was the only fair option. For a quiet life, the stall keeper agreed.

11 (BOATS) They simply tied the loose ends of the rope together. Therefore, there is an identical weight of rope hanging from either side, so the right-hand side will now always be the heavier.

21 Turn two of the gloves inside-out. This will give you two pairs of ordinary gloves.

31 (BOATS) The product was adult videos, and the firm didn't sell any because they were deemed too obscene to send legally through the post. However, the highly suggestive name of the company appeared prominently on all its banker's drafts. Many people didn't present the drafts to the bank, because of their murky origins, so the firm made a profit from all the uncashed drafts. This really did happen in Australia, and the Australian police were unable to recommend a prosecution.

41 (BOATS) The man was demonstrating the strength of the windows to the visitors. The staff in the building told police he had done this several times before, for the amusement of previous visitors.

51 (BOATS) The hotel resident spotted that the chainsaw was electric, and it wasn't plugged in...

61 The insect would probably be more co-operative by being attracted towards the light of the torch, rather than being cajoled with any of the other implements.

71 (BOATS) It's not impossible if the May Queen is a boy. This puzzle was inspired by a number of recent true instances when men have taken part in, and won, beauty contests, because the rules did not prohibit them from entering.

81 The fact that the chamber loaded with the bullet is heavier than the empty chambers means that the loaded chamber is more likely to end up at the bottom when it is spun.

Therefore, either player might work out that, by holding the gun upsidedown, it is more likely that the bullet will stop in line with the firing pin of the gun.

Because the player being aimed at has his back to the player with the gun when the barrel is spun, the firing player can exploit this "hold the gun upsidedown" trick without the other player ever knowing... unless the other player happens to work it out by himself as well.

91 You can buy bars individually at nineteen cents apiece, or packs of seven bars for a dollar. Nobody ever buys six bars at a time because it's cheaper to buy a pack of seven, which contains one extra bar.

BOATS = Based on a true story

ANSWERS TO PUZZLES ENDING IN –2

2 (BOATS) The driver's team mate was in second place, and there was no real need for him to do a risky overtaking move. This form of payment is used in many real-life sports, as an incentive for team driving rather than individual gain.

12 The 29th of February in the year 2116. The year 2000 is a leap year, but the year 2100 is not.

22 The strongest man in the world had said "No man is stronger than me" to Alan, and the weakest man in the world had said, "No man is weaker than me" to Alan. Alan therefore assumed that "no man", or Norman as he had misheard it, was the second strongest man in the world.

32 The shop was a video hire library, and the boxes on the shelves were completely empty. The paying public used the library by taking the video boxes to the counter, and the actual video tapes were kept by the staff behind the counter.

42 While there are no lights in the room, it is a bright day outside. Reg is a slow reader, and needs to follow each line word-by-word by using his finger.

52 (BOATS) Wycliffe had already been dead for over thirty years. His remains were dug up, burned and thrown into a river near his home.

62 Susan placed her hands over the horse's eyes. Not even the wildest or angriest of animals would run anywhere if it couldn't see where it was going.

64 (BOATS) In order to decrease congestion, the traffic authorities only allow cars with odd-numbered registrations on the 1st, 3rd, 5th etc. day of the month, and vice versa for even-numbered number plates. Using the appropriate car, the man can always drive around town despite the restrictions. Such a scheme has been run in several capital cities, including Paris and Athens.

74 The skyscraper was made up of two, twin towers connected by corridor walkways at certain points up the towers.

Each tower started on different levels, so the numbering was different even though I had not actually moved up or down any distance.

84 (BOATS) When these special mortgages were offered, the building society made sure they sold an equal number of "normal" variable rate mortgages also. Whenever the building society put up their rates for a normal variable rate mortgage, this would cancel out the lost income from the reduction in the rate of the special offer mortgage.

94 (BOATS) The building is a garage in the heart of Chelsea, London. So, many people, desperate for their own guaranteed parking space, were prepared to pay the inflated price.

BOATS = Based on a true story

ANSWERS TO PUZZLES ENDING IN –5

5 (BOATS) A poisonous snake dropped from an overhanging tree onto the deck of the boat. All the passengers on board ran away from the snake. This made one side of the boat much, much heavier than the other, and the boat capsized.

15 No! If he did, then he would be able to drink Reg's $3 double whisky for $2, but he would have to pay Reg an extra $3 on top of that as a result of the last bet – paying Reg $5 for a $3 double whisky.

25 (BOATS) The sign was on the side of the *Titanic* – not the real one, but one built using computer graphics for James Cameron's film.

Because the ship appeared with the name CINATIT on its side in one particular shot, this key sequence had to be completely regenerated.

Reportedly, another scene had to be reshot because the ship was seen going down with its propellers still revolving – this was historically inaccurate.

Both these errors cost a tidy sum to correct.

35 (BOATS) As you may have been able to work out from the illustration, she was supposed to jump out of a huge cake, but had suffocated after waiting for an hour inside the sealed dessert.

45 He had asked for twenty dozen buns, but a baker's dozen contains thirteen, not twelve, meaning one extra bun in each dozen.

55 (BOATS) They were written entirely in code, and it took 150 years before cryptology had advanced enough to crack Pepys's code.

65 (BOATS) The thoughtless thief tried to pay the bail using a large number of small coins, which presumably were stolen from the vending machines.

75 Murphy was a ticket inspector at the train station. He caught a pair of fare dodgers and took their names. The tramp was illegally re-selling one-day passes which previous passengers had thrown away. Murphy rang to let his boss know that this activity was taking place.

85 (BOATS) The man was always considerate enough to leave the toilet seat down for his wife. However, every time he went into the bathroom for his shower he noticed that the seat had been left up, presumably by a less chivalrous gentleman...

95 He said "I think the lights around here are dim because someone's got an illegal hook-up to your lights, and is stealing your electricity." The council sent some workmen out to investigate. While they were there, the workmen thought they might as well fix the lights at the same time.

BOATS = Based on a true story

ANSWERS TO PUZZLES ENDING IN –6

6 One of them should run the first lap in the inside lane, and the other in the outside lane. This way, they each run the same distance. As the inside lane is quicker, it shouldn't cause problems with the two bumping into each other when the two swap lanes at the end of lap one.

16 Benny must win the fourth frame (chance 50%) and the fifth frame (chance: 50% x 50%=25%) in order to win. So he should get 25% of the prize ($75), leaving $225 for Berry.

26 (BOATS) Nigeria is a republic, and has no royal family.

36 (BOATS) Suppose the brothers were Jack and John. Jack confesses to the murder, but calls John as his only witness. John confesses at that trial, and Jack's case falls through because there is reasonable doubt. Naturally, murder charges are then brought against John, but John calls Jack as his only witness. Jack confesses at John's trial, and John's case is also thrown out. It is clear that they must have lied, so they received sentences for perjury, but it was impossible to convict them for murder.

46 (BOATS) The bingo caller was dyslexic.

56 (BOATS) The man sent a pager message saying "You have won £500 on the lottery. Call this number... to claim your reward." The thief duly called the phone number given (the victim's home), and he was subsequently arrested when he tried to claim his winnings at the victim's house.

66 (BOATS) Compasses point towards magnetic North, rather than the geographic North Pole. The difference between magnetic North and geographic North is usually a matter of a few degrees, but in some areas of the world they can be in entirely different directions. This is why the deviation of magnetic North is printed on all maps.

76 (BOATS) The man looked at the signature on the parking ticket and noticed that he had been given a ticket by his wife!

86 You can't deduce anything about his name at all. He might not even be a "Bill" at all. Taking the whole of each sentence to be true or false as stated, whichever side you start with the two sentences are contradictions.

96 (BOATS) His mother was in the car with him. However, she suddenly collapsed, and the boy had the presence of mind to steer the car so that it stayed on the road.

BOATS = Based on a true story

ANSWERS TO PUZZLES
ENDING IN –7

7 The man was a native Hawaiian who only knew the Hawaiian alphabet, which is made up of the letters A, E, H, I, K, L, M, N, O, P, U and W. While this was fine for the names of my friends, he had difficulty spelling my name (Chris Dickson), having been told it over the telephone.

17 Dodson lived up to his company's name and hid a clue in the penultimate letter of each line. Berry was the murderer in this case.

27 (BOATS) As there were no tracks in the snow, it must have been an inside job. In this true story, it turned out that the man who reported the crime was in fact the criminal.

37 (BOATS) When the man let go of the rope, he held on tightly to lower the barrel down gently. However, the tools were much heavier than he was, so he was whisked up to the top until his fingers jammed in the pulley. When the barrel hit the ground, some of the tools fell out, and the man (still holding the rope) landed on his back after the return journey. In pain, he let go of the rope, only to be hit on the head by the barrel some moments later.

47 (BOATS) The signalman started tapping out CQD, which was the traditional maritime distress call of the time. However, as SOS had just been recommended by an international convention, the man decided to change to that half-way through the night. The ocean liner was the *Titanic* and this was the first time in history that SOS had been used.

57 (BOATS) Suppose you thought the average would be 50, then the winning

number would be two-thirds of this, namely 33. So you should enter 33 as the answer, but if everyone else did this then the winning number would be 22... and so on until you get down to 1. So the question relies on judgement of other people's instinct. A number between 8 and 15 usually wins.

67 The offer was "New Bigger Bottle". The company manufactured bottles in 400 ml sizes, and refill bags at 500 ml. Customers had complained that they couldn't fit the refill bag's contents into the bottle. The company responded to these complaints by increasing the size of the bottle accordingly. However, the trading standards officials thought that the claim "New Bigger Bottle" should mean there was more softener in the bottle also.

77 It's impossible to make all the legs of the chair level by stacking the blocks on end (it's possible to extend one leg by 10 inches and three legs by 12 inches, but not one leg by 12 inches and three legs by 10 inches).

Given that I was successful, the solution must have involved turning one of the wooden blocks on its side.

87 They had set up three bonfires in an equilateral triangle, which is recognized by pilots all around the world as a distress signal.

97 (BOATS) The model went to bed for a good night's sleep. Humans can be up to two inches shorter in the evening than in the morning, due to the compression of the discs in the spine. When we go to sleep, the discs return to their normal size.

BOATS = Based on a true story

ANSWERS TO PUZZLES ENDING IN –8

8 (BOATS) The promoter flew from Japan to the USA, and got on the same flight as the rock star. A trip around the world for the sake of a few yards.

18 Reg said, "I shall prove this is a perfectly ordinary coin like so. You see the head side there? I shall now turn it over...". He did so to reveal the tail side face up. At this point he turned it over so that the head side ended up face up!

28 Montreal, Moscow, then Los Angeles. The smuggler has been visiting cities in the order in which they hosted the Summer Olympic Games.

38 Mrs Gerrard, so depressed at recent events, tried to take her own life by connecting up the exhaust to inside her car and letting the engine run. However, the car ran out of petrol before too much carbon monoxide was created, so her life was saved.

48 (BOATS) The man had beaten his own wife and set fire to his own home. The woman had forgiven her husband before the trial began, but the jury still convicted him.

58 For safety reasons, left-handed people are not allowed to play polo, due to the collision of mallets that would be possible if two people of opposite handedness were riding side-by-side. By getting two teams of four left-handed players together, the safety aspect was no longer a problem.

68 Mr Dax had "helped" Mr Edgar to rest by giving him a sleeping pill. Having weakened the bolt on the door-frame with a chisel some time ago, in the middle of the night, he opened the lock from the outside by gripping the key with pointed pliers and pressed the door open, breaking the door-frame round the bolt. He strangled Mr Edgar and then re-locked the door through the keyhole, leaving the bolt so it appeared to be broken for the first time by his shoulder charge.

78 The clocks chiming 156 times chime once at 1 o'clock, twice at 2 o'clock and so forth, bearing in mind one o'clock, two o'clock, etc. happen twice each day. The clocks chiming 180 times daily chime once on each half hour, and the clock chiming 228 times a day chimes once at quarter to and quarter past each hour as well.

88 Cunning Reg won a first, a second and a third prize for his guess; everyone receiving a second prize got a third prize as well, so no more than 62 players won the second prize. As we know that $497 was split into a number of prizes each of a whole number of dollars, either 7 players won $71 or 71 players won $7 – no other combination produces round numbers. The latter is impossible from the first sentence, so the former must be true. Cunning Reg won one of the 7 second prizes, so six players must have selected exactly four letters used in the word.

98 (BOATS) In 1897, the General Assembly of Indiana passed a bill ruling that the value of pi (π), the ratio of the circumference of a circle to its diameter, was 4. As the true value of pi is, by definition, **always** 3.1415927..., any engineering calculation using 4 instead would be wildly incorrect.

BOATS = Based on a true story

ANSWERS TO PUZZLES ENDING IN –9

9 (BOATS) *One Man* was the name of a horse, much-loved by racegoers, who died in 1998. The headlines announcing the animal's death were on the front pages of many sports newspapers the next day.

19 For a coin with an odd number of sides, and each side curved in the correct fashion, the diameter of the coin is the same whichever way it points.

For a coin with an even number of sides, the coin might be oriented in two possible ways:

29 He sent a greeting card and a stamped addressed envelope, and invited Timothy to sign the card and send it on using the envelope provided.

Timothy licked the gum on the envelope to make it adhesive and by doing so consumed some very potent poison that was mixed with the adhesive.

39 The cold virus would not exist in the Arctic, because the atmosphere is so cold there that it is sterile.

49 Betty was not asleep but in fact had sadly died. When your heart beats, a few ounces of blood accelerate around your circulation, which would cause the scales to move. No variation in weight implies no heartbeat.

59 (BOATS) When the burglar was trying to see if anyone was in, he put his ear against the window to listen for any noise. A policeman managed to convict the criminal by matching the ear-prints on the windows to that of the criminal.

69 When they laid out the slabs, the artists left a small gap (one inch, say) between each section. This means that, after just 13 of the 200 sections, they are having to move each slab one foot, and the last sections will have to be moved over 16 feet!

This diagram should help demonstrate the principle:

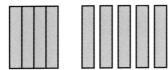

79 He had come from the CAROUSEL, and was intending to CAROUSE later that night, using COARSE language. He AROSE this morning to steal EARS of corn from the field, with the intention of going to SEA using his qualification as an AS (Able Seaman). Then the S balloon burst to leave only A.

89 (BOATS) In each country, he bought the appropriate international car registration badge. By the time he had reached Sweden, he had collected RI, CH, A, R, D, H, U, GH, E and S. His name was Richard Hughes.

99 The Italian man thought the "£1m" asking price was £1,000, and not £1,000,000 as it really was. In many countries, m is used to stand for 1000 (derived from the word mille).

This is why "mn." is sometimes used to represent "million", to prevent confusion.

BOATS = Based on a true story

ANSWERS TO PUZZLES ENDING IN –0

10 (BOATS) My friend and his father didn't take the width of the picture into account, so the pictures were not evenly spaced. This exaggerated diagram shows how the middle third of the wall contains more picture area than the other two:

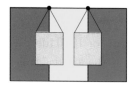

20 The liquid in the drink below the ice cube was made from a syrupy low-alcohol liqueur.

Reg had then carefully poured a stronger, pure spirit on top, ensuring that the two layers didn't mix.

Ice cubes normally float on top of most drinks, but this was an ice cube made from the same substance as the bottom layer.

30 (BOATS) The plug. In 1978, a dredging gang removed the plug from the Chesterfield Canal near Nottingham, England, and millions of gallons of water from a mile and a half of the waterway drained into the nearby River Idle.

40 (BOATS) The town hall official asked for "fanfare" music, but the facilities manager thought the official said "funfair" music!

50 Indianapolis and other towns in most of the counties within Indiana don't observe daylight savings time. While New York operates on Eastern Summer Time, Indianapolis doesn't move its clocks an hour ahead, and so acts as if it's in the next time zone along during the summer. Berry forgets this fact every year.

60 (BOATS) The cheeky fellow had reduced the height of the car enough so that it could fit underneath the automatic barriers at his local car park. The modifications saved him £10 ($16) a week in parking fees.

70 (BOATS) The fact that it was raining outside is not relevant: the tent was indoors all the time. The man was in an oxygen tent, a controversial treatment which he thinks will help extend his life span, but his friends aren't so sure. The diagram that illustrates this question is the warning symbol for oxygen, or oxidizing material.

80 (BOATS) The crook had tried too hard to make his withdrawal look real. He had written the note on the back of one of his own withdrawal slips, which were personalized with his name, address and bank account number...

90 As 36 people without bags take up the same amount of room as 24 people with bags, it's reasonable to assume there are 12 seats which can each take two people with shopping or three people without. The eighteen with shopping would take up nine of these seats, meaning that only three seats remain for nine people without bags to sit on. This leaves 11 people without shopping to stand, which is acceptable by the regulations, so all the shoppers can ride the tram this time.

100 The drivers were taking part in the Formula One Monaco Grand Prix, which takes place on a track formed from some of Monaco's public highways. (The map in the question is of Monaco.)

BOATS = Based on a true story

ABOUT THE AUTHOR

Chris M. Dickson was born in the north of England in 1975. He has been devising games and puzzles for over five years.

He writes a regular column for the postal gaming magazine *Flagship*, and runs postal games of his own creation. He regularly organizes and participates in board game conventions around the UK.

He recently completed a degree in Mathematical Sciences at Oxford University.

Email: chris@dickson.demon.co.uk